JON MITCHELL
BRIGHT AND BREEZY
YTV IN ALL WEATHERS

featuring
CALENDAR, EMMERDALE, HEARTBEAT
AND THE ROYAL

With contributions from
AUSTIN MITCHELL,
CHRIS CHITTELL
AND DEREK FOWLDS

**YORKSHIRE
TELEVISION**

itv Calendar

Celebrating 40 years of Calendar and YTV

GREAT-N-ORTHERN

Great Northern Books Limited
PO Box 213, Ilkley, LS29 9WS

www.greatnorthernbooks.co.uk

ISBN: 978 1 905080 56 4

Design and layout: David Burrill

Printed in Germany

CIP Data

A catalogue for this book is available from the British Library

CONTENTS

FOREWORD

I'm constantly amazed at the quality and quantity of weather-related photographs that are sent to me at my weather office on a daily basis by our dedicated band of viewers. No less amazing is the technology that allows those photos, and in some cases movies, to be sent to me hours if not minutes after the event has occurred, thus giving them 'real-time' relevance in my weather forecasts for *Calendar*.

Who would have imagined this possible back in 1968 when Yorkshire Television first took to the airwaves? Back then people didn't take many photos because film was expensive and certainly just about all my family photos were taken in black and white at that time. I've no doubt that some notable weather events were photographed by the viewers of the new Yorkshire Television and sent in via the Royal Mail to be somehow put onto film for broadcast, but this would be days if not weeks after the event and would hardly be newsworthy. It wasn't just family snaps that were in black and white in those days either, most televisions were too. In fact as late as 1971 there was only one posh kid in our class at school who had a colour telly. Imagine what the weather photos would look like in black and white – not very exciting I should think.

Keep them coming by the way (weatherphotos@itv.com). I simply cannot get enough of them!

It was then suggested that I put the best of these images together in a calendar (Debbie Lindley and I did exactly that back in 1997). Brilliant idea, but this presents two problems: how does one choose the best twelve, or at most, thirteen images from the thousands I have received and moreover the said calendar would only last a year before being discarded. So why not bring together, not necessarily the most technically superior, but indeed the most appealing images in a 'coffee table' book? What's more, as Yorkshire Television is celebrating its 40th birthday in 2008, why not combine that book with how weather presentations have developed over those forty years and how the elements have affected outdoor filming of Yorkshire TV productions such as Emmerdale, Heartbeat and The Royal? Well why not indeed? So here it is.

I am delighted that proceeds from this book are being donated to the Yorkshire Air Ambulance and the Lincolnshire and Nottinghamshire Air Ambulance. As a patron of the Yorkshire Air Ambulance I have seen first hand the critical work these independent charities deliver each day across the ITV Yorkshire Region. Quite simply they provide a life saving service and a vital role in a 999 situation.

The counties within our region have vast and beautiful landscapes that not only include isolated and rural locations, as many of the pictures in this book show, but also major

A Lincolnshire & Nottinghamshire Air Ambulance helicopter seen shortly after touch down, and two Yorkshire Air Ambulance helicopters in flight. Both charities will benefit from proceeds from the sale of this book.

(Photo: BBC)

motorways and populated cities. In a medical emergency these air ambulances can carry a patient to the nearest hospital in about ten minutes, or the most relevant hospital within fifteen. Getting patients to the treatment that they need so quickly has proved to save lives.

However, both charities rely on the generosity of donations as the lifeblood of their service. To maintain and keep just one air ambulance in the air costs thousands of pounds each day, and without the support that both charities receive they would not be able to continue their life-saving work for which they are known.

I have thoroughly enjoyed choosing the photographs for this book and doing so has only served to reinforce my belief that we are so lucky to live in such a beautiful part of the world – a part enjoying a wide variety of weather that often enhances the landscape. I hope you enjoy the book too.

Jon Mitchell, August 2008

CALENDAR – THE EARLY YEARS

Austin Mitchell, who was there virtually at the beginning, looks back at the birth of Yorkshire Television and *Calendar* and recalls days when the weather did its worst.

THE start of Yorkshire Television in July 1968 was comparable as a contribution to the history of TV to the prolonged interference on John Logie Baird's minute TV screen after his very first broadcast when the scanning wheel stopped scanning. Tours of the studio got lost because the building work was still going on and climbing over piles of bricks had not been billed as part of the royal itinerary. The Duchess of Kent got stuck in one of the new lifts, the TV link with the lavish reception and dance in Leeds University failed, and the highlight of the day, the very first edition of *Calendar*, broke down. It was presented by Jonathan Aitken, described by *New Society* as an urbane metropolitan presence for a Yorkshire tea table, but someone who shouldn't have been there at all because he was also Conservative candidate for Thirsk and Malton – and hence precluded from presenting a local current affairs programme. Jonathan announced the dynamic new Yorkshire programme and managed a nervous smile before the film broke and the screen faded to black.

Pearl Harbour would live on in the annals of infamy. The first *Calendar* can't even enter the disaster stakes because the tape was wisely scrubbed. But it was a triumph compared to what was to come. After staggering on for a few days, during which the Head of News went hysterical and locked himself in his office, the technicians went on strike. Managers, who had as yet no experience of managing, struggled to put out anything that came to hand, including Test Card C and trial programmes recorded at Batley Variety Club as part of staff training. *Calendar* closed down and its eager young team retreated to the trouser factory across the road.

This was the point at which I came in, not to save *Calendar* but to save my own sanity. I was in Oxford and saw nothing of the disaster, just like the rest of the dons who would never admit to watching television even if they actually did, and for whom Yorkshire was a distant and almost certainly dim world of which they knew nothing. I was offered £12 a day to come

Austin Mitchell (right) joined *Calendar* after the first week. He is seen here during those early days with co-presenter Richard Whiteley.

and work on *Calendar* for the summer, starting only when the strike was over. Smallest pay but best offer I've ever had. It was also the start of the happiest time of my life. Nothing is more exciting than daily live television. It's a heightened adrenalin rushed existence like living on the edge of a precipice. No job is better than creating something new with a talented team coming together.

The BBC had stolen a considerable lead on Yorkshire Television by dint of splitting their *Look North* programme – previously covering the North from Manchester – and creating a Leeds edition that came on air a couple of months before YTV's starting date. This gave them a considerable lead in the ratings war, particularly when Yorkshire's fell after the first disastrous week.

Knowing something about opinion polls I took on the job of measuring the ratings, which then came in big green books containing the reports from two thousand monitored TV sets all over the country. In practice this system favoured ITV because it gave more weight than would face-to-face interviews to sets that were left switched on but unwatched. This was because the owners were either out of the room or the house or indulging in all the other dimensions of human activity that can and still do go on in front of an unwatched TV screen. Since householders who behaved like this were considered lower down the social scale, it was assumed – probably correctly – that the unwatched sets were switched to ITV!

Yet even on our biased measure the *Calendar* audience was well behind BBC's *Look North* until November when we began to catch up and the new year 1969 when we actually overtook them. My weekly assessments became even more cheerful until suddenly disaster struck.

THE NIGHT THE MAST FELL DOWN

In the bitter winter conditions of March 1969 the super new mast, constructed specially for the Yorkshire contract by the IBA on Emley Moor, fell down. It had been crippled by the enormous weight of ice built up by the Yorkshire winter – something of a severity the IBA had clearly never considered. The news came through suddenly, screens all over Yorkshire went blank, crews were dispatched onto the moor to film the twisted wreckage in the dark. and we interviewed the locals who'd managed to evade it falling on them; interviews which unfortunately couldn't go out because we had no pictures.

It was incredible. None of us could quite believe it. From neck and neck in the ratings war we'd collapsed to zilch. Even the unwatched TV sets, which were still switched to ITV, showed only the snowstorm that covers them when transmission fails. No use preparing and performing programmes no one could watch, though in fact we still continued to do so, so great was the sense of unreality.

It lasted a week while the IBA scrabbled round putting up a mini mast that reached part of

The shattered
remains of
the 1,265ft
Emley Moor
TV mast,
near
Huddersfield,
after its
spectacular
collapse
during an ice
storm on 19
March 1969.

The brand new Emley Moor mast, built in 1972 and resembling a giant lighthouse
made of white concrete. A dominant landmark over much of West Yorkshire, its
visibility – or lack of it – acts as a local weather barometer.

the area and the management made up its mind what to do. We were all called into the huge and empty studio to be addressed by the MD, Ward Thomas, who told us to carry on producing because everyone was working hard to get back on the air.

RAIN IN THE DALES

I don't think Barry Cockcroft was there. Barry conquered the Dales and made them his own. It was a conquest which enabled him to submit huge travel claims, occasional films and to work largely unsupervised – a technique he mastered by giving contact numbers for pubs where he had an arrangement that if anyone rang they would say he'd just nipped out to do some research. Once when he was drafted to film in the South Pacific I rang the Spring Rock Inn in Elland to be told that Barry had just nipped out and would be back shortly!

The great charm of filming with Barry was that it was such a leisurely affair staying at the best hotels in the Dales – for in those days television companies had money and spent it – with long leisurely lunches at carefully selected best restaurants. Hours were spent admiring the view while his preferred cameraman, Mustapha Hammuri, an artist with film totally out of place on 'Yorkshireness' stories of strikes and industrial disasters, took beautiful shots. These never appeared in the final film, usually hacked down from the hour Mustapha intended to a bowdlerised four minutes, the longest time span Fred Bull, the butcher turned film editor, would ever envisage.

Small wonder that wherever we were – Hull or Halifax – Mustapha was constantly urging us to film in the Arabian Gulf where, he assured us, we would all be given gold watches almost as good as his by grateful sheikhs. Sadly, it proved difficult to film items of Yorkshire interest in the Gulf so he was reduced to more mundane subjects, like the horn man of Bainbridge who supposedly has been blowing his horn to bring the sheep home every day since the Middle Ages. Jack Metcalfe looked old enough to have done exactly that but where the spirit was willing the flesh was weak. The day we filmed him it poured most of the day and our massive team of ten spent it in the pub plying the horn man with whisky. When there was a brief break in the weather he was unable to stand up, let alone blow, which was perhaps fortunate because it was too dark to film in any case.

The next day we moved on from this triumph to Semerwater, where Barry had hired boats, lights, aqualungs and wet suits so that I could be filmed seeking the sunken city underwater. Then, too, it rained all day and the brown, brackish water was so impenetrable nothing could be seen, with the result that I was concussed swimming head on into Mustapha's heavy underwater camera as he swam towards me. Since *National Geographic* has not seen fit to repeat this voyage of discovery, the underwater city remains undiscovered to this day.

BLIZZARD CONDITIONS

Later opportunities came more naturally. Duncan Dallas, who had been hired from the BBC's *Man Alive* programme, taught me the basics of their interviewing technique, which was to remain silent but purse your lips as if blowing a kiss to the interviewees to encourage them to keep talking. He and I did a film of Yorkshire's first, greatest and last pop festival at Krumlin. We spent weeks filming the preparations, the fences, the stage building and the two organisers. Both were living in high hopes of becoming millionaires, despite the difficulties caused by the agents of the big names who wanted cash up front while they had no money, not having yet sold any tickets. This didn't stop them advertising 'A Galaxy of Talent', which did boost advance sales though unfortunately none of them turned up except one weird group. They assured me that they were Pink Floyd, only for me to discover, after wasting nearly an hour of film, they weren't. That typified the whole disaster. There was a nice atmosphere on the first two days, though staff were taking cash at the gates and disappearing with it, huge holes were appearing in the expensive wire fence and the groups were largely unknown. On the Saturday it began to rain so we decided to leave and come back the following day.

When arriving first the next day I discovered there'd been a disaster – an autumn blizzard, heavy snow, intense cold, one camper dying of exposure in the night, the rest departing rather like Napoleon's retreat from Moscow, and the police combing the site for more bodies and any passing drugs. I turned round to set off back for Duncan and the crew but couldn't get through the huddled hordes and stalled cars so I stayed. Duncan arrived to film the empty field when it was all over. No interviews with the organisers. One had walked off into the night in a nervous breakdown, the other was dazed and shell-shocked and we had only fifteen minutes of film to fill the half hour slot we'd been allocated.

Duncan gradually focused on his real interest, science, where I was lucky enough to stay with him despite my Arts degree, which of course gives every holder a total lack of interest in science. So I was able to do more of his documentaries, including an American programme done in the bitter winter of early 1977 when he told me that his expenses wouldn't run to an overcoat for me, only a raincoat, so I could appear more stylish. I nearly froze to death as we interviewed B F Skinner, the famous behaviourist, taking him back to his childhood home to show how children in his day learned by doing things rather than sitting in front of a TV. Having taken Skinner into the woods to show how he learned from snow, we lost him in a huge snowdrift and had to drag him out half dead and cart him home.

FROZEN IN TIME

For me much of the excitement of the *Calendar* years was rediscovering Yorkshire and bringing its basic industries: wool, coal, steel, fishing and strikes, all then in their pomp, to the screen. It was also getting to know and discover its characters, always more individualistic and abrasive than today's smooth men striving to make Yorkshire world class when they'd be better employed making the world Yorkshire class. So we discovered Hannah Hauxwell [the central character in YTV's acclaimed documentary *Too Long a Winter*], who Barry Cockcroft filmed in ever widening circles: Hannah's Dales, Hannah's Yorkshire, Hannah's Europe, Hannah's World.

Hannah Hauxwell as portrayed in the classic 1973 documentary *Too Long a Winter*. The phenomenal public response to the programme jammed the YTV switchboards for two days. It went on to win the Pye Award as the Best Regional Programme of the Year.

Barry mobilised not only his knowledge of the Dales but his entrepreneurial ability in organising the world Knur and Spell championship. There hadn't been such an event since 1926, when it had been a purely Yorkshire occasion, but this included players dredged up from Lancashire as well as numerous and grizzled Yorkshire veterans who needed subtitles to be understood outside Barnsley. Barry wangled a sponsorship from Joe Kagan, who gave us all Gannex Macs like a tribe of Harold Wilson impersonators. They were vitally necessary, for the great day, held on the moors above Elland, was bitter cold, enough to freeze the knurrs off the spellers and nip the iggys of the nipsiers. The players were all hardy moor men, some even played in shirtsleeves, but we were lucky to survive the day with the entire presenter force alive, if only because they were excessively warmed by the huge quantities of whisky Barry doled out.

Great Days. And we were a great vintage, not through any inherent ability but because we were lucky enough to be in the right place at the right time – the start of *Calendar* and Yorkshire Television. No one will spend money in the lavish way we did and money isn't the root of all evil but certainly is of all good television. But we, the lucky ones, shared its great days and created something good. I hope Yorkshire enjoyed it as much as we did.

CALENDAR – 2008

Calendar celebrated its 40th birthday on July 29, 2008 with a special programme featuring some of the biggest stories of the past four decades and a host of guests – presenters, reporters and people who've been in the news. Everyone connected with *Calendar* is proud of the programme and the fantastic and loyal audience it has served down the years. The weather plays a huge part in what we do – whether it's reporting on the floods of 2007, or simply giving viewers up to date forecasts each and every day.
We continue to win major awards and out-perform our rivals. Obviously I'm biased, but I believe Calendar is the best regional news programme in the business and I'd like to pay tribute to the tremendous talent, dedication and professionalism of everyone in the team.

Will Venters, Editor, Calendar

EMMERDALE

Chris Chittell, a keen charity fundraiser who has taken part in umpteen marathons, joined what was then *Emmerdale Farm* in 1986. He plays the character of Eric Pollard, an antiques dealer, factory owner and womaniser once described as 'a swindler and a crook who's conned just about everyone in the village'. He looks back over twenty years of filming in rain and shine:

What really sticks out in the mind is that the weather has rarely defeated us. We seem to cope with torrential downpours and blistering heat, and we only give up when conditions are extreme. Then the problem is usually solved by a quick rewrite in the village hall. About two-thirds of the filming is outdoors and one-third in the studio, and I really enjoy the outdoor work.

When I joined the programme the exterior shots were still being filmed at Esholt, the village in the Aire valley between Leeds and Bradford. It doesn't get much wintry weather, but I remember once riding through the village on horseback in snow. It was very dramatic.

There was another occasion when we were filming outside the Woolpack at seven in the evening and it was so bitterly cold that our lips were freezing. It is hard to do a warm-up when your lips will scarcely move and none of us could talk!

We definitely outstayed our welcome in Esholt. Fans of the programme flocked to the village and started to disrupt the lives of the locals by clogging up roads and car parks. We had to stop filming every time someone wondered into shot or took a photograph with flash – and it all became very difficult.

Snow scene in Arncliffe in 1973. *Emmerdale Farm* – as it was originally called – derived its title from Amerdale, the old name for the valley of Littondale in which Arncliffe is situated. The programme was filmed here from its launch in 1972 but the location proved to be too far from Leeds and the constant disruption was not wholly popular with locals. A move to Esholt was made in 1976.

It was much easier when we moved to Harewood, although many members of the cast still looked back on the days when we were out in other locations. Adele Silva, who played Kelly Windsor, long remembered a scene when her character was having an affair with her schoolteacher, Tom. She recalled: 'The scenes weren't as romantic as they looked. We had to film in this dingy old bedsit place and it was freezing! In one scene, just before Christmas, it was really sub-zero. It was supposed to be all sexy and Kelly was supposed to be provocative and fluttering her eyelashes. It was just so funny because we had thermal tops on and about seven hundred layers of clothes. I had opaque tights because they're supposed to make the skirt look shorter but instead of wearing one pair I had about four pairs on – it was so unflattering!'

Alun Lewis, who played Vic Windsor in the nineties, also often talked about the vagaries of the Yorkshire weather: 'My most memorable moment of filming was being up to the knees in a freezing mountain stream at Bolton Abbey – I was in a torrential waterfall for three days, on and off, for about eight hours a day. I had a wet suit on but it was still cold. I was supposed to have caught my foot under a log under the water. I'll never forget that time. It was March, so you can imagine!'

Once we made the move to Harewood there is one weather-related episode that really does stick in the mind. This is the great New Year storm of 2004, which seriously damaged the Woolpack inn and killed its barmaid Tricia. Mark Charnock (Marlon Dingle) summed it up dramatically: 'They had rain machines, a lightning machine and an incredible wind machine. We did a scene where I'm struggling up the main street of Emmerdale – you couldn't open your eyes the rain was so strong. They wanted to get a really dirty storm going, a life threatening storm and it was like doing a movie. They had this big camera on a track, the lightning machine was going and it was really exciting.'

Emmerdale provides some wonderful memories, although I have to confess that sometimes they all roll into one!

Lambing in the snow at Emmerdale Farm in 1978. Left to right are Joe Sugden (Frazer Hines), Matt Skilbeck (Frederick Pyne) and Dolly Skilbeck (Katharine Barker).

One of the most dramatic episodes in the history of *Emmerdale* occurred in 1993 when a plane crash set fire to much of the village. Filmed over three weeks in freezing conditions, it cost a fortune and tested the skills of the special effects department.

opposite: Jack Sugden (Clive Hornby) braves the winter weather and finds that many of his sheep have been killed in the plane crash. This episode, which also saw off four members of the cast, dramatically boosted viewing figures.

In 2001 melting snow lingers on the main street of Emmerdale, looking for all the world like an authentic Dales village. But this was now an incredibly realistic film set, purpose-built for Emmerdale two years earlier on a 300-acre site on the Harewood estate.

EMMERDALE

Please drive carefully
through our village

EMMERDALE
Home of
TATE
Tours

The attention to detail on the *Emmerdale* set extends to signs instructing non-existent motorists to drive carefully – especially important in deep snow. The quest for authenticity has even extended to placing yoghurt on house roofs, thus encouraging lichen to grow and giving a weathered appearance.

Memorable events occurred early in 2004 when a violent storm struck the village and caused severe damage at the Woolpack inn. Elizabeth Estensen, playing pub landlady Diane, recalls: 'We were filming during the night. It was very cold and as soon as they said it was time for another take the wind machine and the rain machine would start. It was freezing and wet and miserable.'

Left: Barmaid Tricia (Sheree Murphy) battles through the storm to leave the village.

Above: The pub chimney came crashing down on Tricia and she did not survive the storm. Sheree Murphy looks back with mixed memories: 'These scenes were hard work, especially being stuck under the rubble for quite a few hours in the pouring rain and the wind. But I loved every moment of it!'

Disaster struck again in February 2007 when Billy Hopwood (David Crellin) gave Victoria Sugden (Isabel Hodgins) a lift home and found the brakes weren't working. The van plunged into a flooded lake.

HEARTBEAT

Oscar Blaketon, played by Derek Fowlds, in the bar of the Aidensfield Arms.

Derek Fowlds is one of the original cast of *Heartbeat*. An instant success when first broadcast in April 1992, the programme was originally based on a series of books written under the pen-name of Nicholas Rhea and portraying the life of a young village constable in the Yorkshire countryside of the 1960s. Derek plays the part of Oscar Blaketon, who was the dour-faced police sergeant before retiring to run the pub in the fictional village of Aidensfield on the North York Moors:

Goathland was chosen as the location for Aidensfield because it is in a part of the world that had rarely been featured on television before. You get a remarkable contrast there with the purple heather and the soft greens of the fields, but it can be bitterly cold when the wind comes off the North Sea.

When filming started in 1991 I thought I would be there for six months, but I'm still involved over fifteen years later. In the early days there was much more location work and all the usual problems with the weather. Niamh Cussack, who played PC Rowan's wife Kate, once said: 'We don't really mind if the weather is one thing or the other – if it's dull, that's fine, if it's sunny, that's fine but if you get ten minutes of one and half an hour of the other, that's hopeless! Where we are, the weather alters very quickly so we spend a lot of time waiting for it to change.'

We have done many stunts down the years. One of the biggest was a train crash in the snow in an episode called 'Riders of the Storm'. The actual crash was shown and then scenes of the carriage turned on its side and the aftermath.

As pub landlord, I've played in countless pub scenes. These were originally filmed in a hotel in Goathland. We used to use the real interior but eventually we were there too long and we interfered with the chap's business too much so it was recreated as a set. We still had real winters in the 1990s and on two occasions we got snowed in at the hotel. The people of

A snow machine busy in action in Goathland churchyard in readiness for the screen wedding of Gina Ward and Phil Bellamy.

No sooner had the snow machines done their work than it started to snow. Cast and crew alike were taken by surprise.

The magical scene as Gina and Bernie Scripps (Peter Benson) make their way from the Aidensfield Arms to the church in a horse and carriage.

Goathland were wonderful. There was always plenty of whisky – and we had some great times.

We usually did a Christmas episode in July or August. Obviously, Christmas should have snow so this was created artificially and laid all over the place – it was always great fun.

The most memorable occasion with snow was the screen wedding of Gina Ward (played by Tricia Penrose) to PC Phil Bellamy (Mark Jordon). It was filmed in winter to be shown in January 2007, although in fact it was not screened until the following June. Snow machines were brought in at great expense – and then suddenly it started to snow! The real snow took the whole cast and crew by surprise. It certainly changed things.

Mark Jordon commented at the time: 'The weather became atrocious with real snow but they still had to go ahead with the weather machines. The mixture of the machines blowing the fake snow and the actual temperatures being below zero meant that we were absolutely frozen. We were genuinely shaking.'

Although there are usually plenty of laughs on set, Tricia Penrose found the day was more like an endurance test: 'I nearly fell over a few times with my high heels. The wind was blowing in different directions and snow was all over the place. It was bitterly, bitterly cold on location. I can't tell you how cold it was – I could have cried while trying to be all happy and laughing.'

It was a magical day I shall never forget, especially as I had to play a very emotional part.

Oscar Blaketon (Derek Fowlds) is at top right as the wedding party comes down the steps of
the Aidensfield Arms. Tricia Penrose, playing the part of Gina Ward, recalled:
'When we got out of the pub it was really snowing hard. It was awful for me in terms of my
costume, because I had a long white fur cape over my dress that did get a bit wet and muddy.
It certainly took a beating which was quite upsetting. They had to try and keep it as clean as
possible. The snow looked amazing though, it was so picturesque.'

THE ROYAL

The relatively new drama *The Royal* has also had its moments with the weather. For the fifth series, the beauty contest scenes were shot at the Scarborough Spa on a very wet and cold April day in 2005. The contestants had to spend the entire day wearing nothing but 1960s bikinis and stilettos.

There were dramatic scenes at the beginning of the new series of in June 2008 when there was a train crash and the team from *The Royal* had to rush to the rescue. Damian O'Hare, playing the part of Doctor Nick Burnett, recalls: 'We filmed it in a beautiful place near the Yorkshire Dales. It was an arduous two-week shoot, but very exciting. We were hoping to have glorious weather, but it rained solidly and we were up to our knees in mud! It was my first week of filming so it was great to be involved so heavily – I just threw myself into it. Everyone looked after me, although I was sprayed with cold water a few times.'

Kari Corbett, playing Nurse Marina McKaig, gets sprayed with water during the filming of the train crash episode in the new series of *The Royal*.

Opposite: Nurses Stella Davenport (Natalie Anderson) and Marina McCaig gloomily wait under an umbrella during one of the relentless downpours that plagued the filming of the train crash.

'AND NOW FOR THE WEATHER'

Forty years of weather reporting are celebrated by Jon Mitchell, who has presented forecasts on *Calendar* for almost two decades.

When *Calendar* was launched in 1968 there was no weather forecast as such. Instead there were occasional appearances by the legendary Bill Foggitt, who had a huge following due to his often correct predictions based on traditional weather lore and sayings. Clutching a piece of winter jasmine, he would for example insist that the activity of moles meant a bad winter was in prospect. As most winters at the time were 'bad', he impressed all and sundry and became a modern-day equivalent of Mother Shipton.

The next stage was a regular forecast – only it was delivered by telephone from the Bawtry Met Office, which covered most of north-east England. A photograph of the forecaster appeared on screen along with his captioned name, and this alternated with a weather-appropriate landscape picture. Mistakes were common and confused viewers often saw a photograph of a sunny field bearing the forecaster's name!

Change came with the closure of Bawtry and its replacement by a new weather centre in Leeds. This led YTV to ask the Met Office if it would supply a forecaster to present the weather on *Calendar*. It was a big step forward, although by comparison with today it was still the dark ages and much of the forecaster's time was spent analysing hand-plotted charts.

Presentation of the forecast went through several phases of trial and error before settling on a revolving weather cube. Its four faces displayed a large satellite picture, a hand-drawn weather map and two regional maps – one for that day and one for the next. Herein lay one of the major drawbacks, as the overall weather situation was limited to the next twenty-four hours.

Another problem centred round the satellite image, which was received at the weather centre on a fax machine the size of a domestic oven. It was then sent by courier to the local photographic processing company and placed on rigid card. It next went to YTV studios, where it was filmed by a special camera for insertion into the forecast. All this effort represented less

What the viewer doesn't see! The big blank blue screen, which gives the impression that I am turning to a weather chart. All I can see is blue, so I have to refer to the TV monitor. The red cross on the studio floor is where I must stand in order for the lighting to be correct.

than ten seconds of airtime, although a more fundamental drawback was that the image could be up to six hours old by the time it was transmitted. This is a long time in the fast-moving world of the weather forecast.

The big change in TV weather forecasts came with the advent of computer-generated graphics. As these became more powerful, it was possible to show animated weather symbols and such features as rain falling from moving clouds. When I became a weather forecaster in 1978 we spent most of our time plotting charts with two pens sellotaped together – the finished product was a work of art that took three solid hours sitting at a desk to complete! These days a computer can source all the weather data and print out a similar chart in a matter of seconds. Today my office consists of just computer screens and very little paper, and is a great disappointment to most visitors.

Even the studio is not quite what it seems to the viewer. As can be seen on the photograph on this page, there is a big blue screen behind me. When I turn to the left, it gives the impression that I am turning to the weather chart but in fact there is just this blank background. There is nothing behind me to look at, but this difficulty is overcome by a small TV monitor just out of camera shot on which I see both my hand and the weather map. I have to remember never to wear anything blue – and more than once I have had to change a tie at the very last moment!

MORE AND MORE WEATHER

I got into weather forecasting at an early age. I was born and brought up in Morecambe and went to Lancaster Road primary school, where Eric Morecambe had earlier been a pupil. This is where I often burst into song: 'Bring me sunshine…' We had a weather station at Lancaster Road and by the age of seven or eight I was the weather monitor. Everyone else wanted to be weather monitor and we had to take it in turns, but after a week everyone else became bored and no longer wanted to do it, yet I was still interested. So I carried on, and continued to record all the thermometer and rainfall readings. As a teenager I became fascinated by books on clouds and soon got to know all the classifications.

My careers master at Grammar school cottoned on to my interest and one day he saw a job advertised in the Met Office. I applied for it and was subsequently offered the job. After a number of years at Heathrow and Manchester Airports I was posted to the Leeds Weather Centre in 1986. From 1989 the YTV forecasts were sponsored and thus it became essential for the regular presenter Bob Rust to have a stand-in when he went on holiday. A notice went up in the Weather Centre asking for volunteers but no one came forward. Bob kept asking me and I kept refusing. Then one day he rang me up after I had been on nightshift and was just coming round from a deep sleep. 'Come down for an audition at YTV,' he said.

Throughout my informative years I found these two books very inspirational – *The Ladybird Book of Weather* and *The Observers' Book of Weather*. I've no doubt older readers will recognise them instantly. People often ask me to recommend simple books on the weather to inspire their younger relations. I suppose to a youngster these books must look terribly old-fashioned but I have to say, even to this day, they take some beating in their brevity and concise approach to what can be a complicated science. I just love them, won't hear a word said against them and they can still be picked up in second-hand bookshops for a bargain price!

No mention of Charlie's Angels please!

One of the best aspects of my job is being part of this wonderful weather team at ITV.

Kerrie Gosney, Debbie Lindley, Jo Blythe and myself have all got along famously for many years now and I consider myself very lucky to count them all as good friends as well as colleagues. Debbie is the joker among us and, as anybody who has heard her on the radio will know, she's daft as a brush!

The presenters are the familiar faces to those watching at home, but our weather forecasts – and indeed *Calendar* itself – would not be able to radiate into the ether from the top of Emley Tower without the many dozens of team members working behind the scenes. Technical staff work day in day out alongside us and make our job all the more pleasant with their professionalism and sense of humour. Many of them say they couldn't do my job – well I tell you what, I couldn't do theirs. They all deserve medals.

Out in all weathers! Doing a live broadcast in Scarborough when the conditions didn't quite match the summer shorts.

I now realise why police do dawn raids, as I was put on the spot and didn't offer any resistance. Just to get Bob off the phone, I agreed and in the absence of anyone better I soon found myself in front of a camera, so to this day I'm eternally grateful to Bob for his persistence. My first forecast was presented live and was quite daunting. I remember being terribly nervous and thinking why on earth was I putting myself through this ordeal. Standing in front of a million people certainly got the adrenalin going. It is essential to present a good forecast and at the same time be entertaining and informative. I may have been the latter at the time, but I'm reasonably sure I wasn't the former!

The regular presenters of *Calendar* in 1989 were Richard Whiteley and Christa Ackroyd. Richard used to keep me on my toes because the other presenters and I had a rehearsal when the link-in to the weather was decided. But not Richard – simply because he didn't know what he was going to say. So I had to think very quickly when the time came to throw to me.

I remember one day when he had been to the hairdresser's. Turning to me with his usual 'And now for the weather with Jon', he then added, 'Do you like my new hair cut?' Quick as a flash I replied, 'It will be nice when it's finished, Richard.' I don't think he was terribly suited, although he did laugh, and I was quite proud of myself.

When Bob Rust retired I became a regular weather presenter along with Debbie Lindley. Working with Debbie was very enjoyable; I taught her the intricacies of meteorology and she taught me how to be a better presenter. As the public's interest in weather grew, so did the number of forecasts and presenters. Today there are forecasts in the late morning, lunchtime, mid-afternoon, teatime at the end of *Calendar* and also after the late evening *Calendar*.

In addition to these we produce pollen forecasts and ultra-violet (sunburn) forecasts in the summer – and all this covering seven days a week. We have our work cut out, so much so that we have a team of four here in the ITV weather office consisting of Jo Blythe and Kerrie Gosney in addition to Debbie and myself.

There is also the very popular *Live Weather Chat* every night on *Calendar* when I am sat on the sofa so that I can be verbally abused by my co-presenters as well as talk about everyday things. These are mostly concerned with the weather but I am sometimes also allowed to embrace my passion for steam locomotives and the outdoors in the thread 'A Breath of Fresh Air'. In addition I produce two forecasts a day for the website (itvlocal.com/yorkshire), which I believe is the way forward.

There is rarely a dull moment. Some of the most exciting times have been going to places the public can't normally visit, such as the top of Emley Moor TV mast, inside Ferrybridge power station, or on top of Ribblehead viaduct – one of the windiest places in Britain.

I have to be very careful when giving a forecast and using such terms as 'warm' and 'cold'. To one person standing at a bus stop it will be cold, and next to him will be someone digging a hole and finding it hot and sweaty. It is therefore better to give the actual temperature. It is very difficult in the summer as it is naturally assumed that people like hot and sunny weather, but not everyone does. I recently said on *Calendar* that it was a perfect day – the temperature was about eighteen, it was lovely and clear with sunshine, a light breeze blowing and just a little bit of fair weather cumulus. Then Christine Talbot, one of my co-presenters, said: 'Well, I was at my daughter's sports day and I thought it was actually a bit cold.' So you see I can't please everybody and have to be careful in my descriptions.

PICTURES FROM VIEWERS

We started including viewers' pictures in the forecasts about six years ago with the advent of email and digital cameras. It suddenly struck us how easy it would be to feature such pictures in the bulletins. They give a real time feel to the forecast, as we can say 'This is what it was like earlier today in Scarborough' or 'This was sunrise this morning over Lincoln'. They also make the forecast more relevant and involve the viewers. Everyone likes to see their name and the town or village where they live on television.

The number and quality of the pictures has improved as digital cameras have become more generally available. Now we are often spoilt for choice but it can be feast or famine. On December 4, 2007, there was a magnificent sunset around teatime just as people were returning home from work. It was so dramatic we went outside with our own cameras, but the upshot was that my emails were completely jammed the following day. On other days I can be lucky to receive two or three pictures. Even pictures of rain, low cloud, mist and fog can be interesting if thought about and composed well, so I do hope that 'bad' weather will not deter viewers from sending photos to me.

LIGHTER MOMENTS

I soon realised that as a nation we are obsessed with the weather. How could it be otherwise, as so often a walk or a picnic is ruined by a sudden downpour. People who recognise me in the street will often come up and say, 'What's the weather going to be like today, Jon?' This is followed by: 'I bet you get fed up of people asking you that." Well actually I don't. I usually have a stab at some kind of brief forecast but I include a big caveat: 'I haven't seen a weather chart for a few days, so I might be a bit out.' Some of my more cheeky colleagues might comment, 'So what's new there then!' However, the point is that people are nice to me ninety-nine per cent of the time and realise what a hard job we have, despite all the latest technology, in trying to second-guess Mother Nature.

There have been many memorable happenings down the years, several of them involving winter weather. My neighbour frequently reminds me of the time I had my car stuck in the snow and how he gained great satisfaction from a weatherman having to dig his way out of a drift to get to work. I even proposed in snow and despite the conditions I got down on one knee. Thankfully, Thankfully, my girlfriend accepted but it was so cold! It is hard being a weatherman's wife, as she has just got to lie back and think of England, Wales, Northern Ireland and southern parts of Scotland!

This is all that was left of club rooms at Riddings Junior School, Scunthorpe, after they were struck by a mini tornado on 13 December 2000. The group photo shows (left to right) Ernie Gash, John Creek, Royce Coates, Mick Butler and Dave Spackman in front of a still standing wall and a replica nameplate displaying their attitude to what happened. Just over a year later I agreed to broadcast live from their new rooms 'in an attempt to explain why I did not warn them of its coming'! (But in reality it was just an excuse to have a go on their wonderful and extensive model railway layout!)

Then there was the time at the Weather Centre when we used to ring up local councils to warn them of icy roads. One day a lady answered the phone and I asked her to copy the warning down word for word. She did so and then said, 'It's very good of the Met Office to ring everyone up and warn them of ice on the road.' I enquired, 'Is this so-and-so council?' She replied, 'No it's not. I'm just Mrs Bloggs down the road.' I'd got the wrong number and she thought I was going through the phone book to ring everyone up and warn them of icy roads! Bless her!

On another occasion I commented on air that the snow had been the worst of the winter, some roads were impassable and local councils were 'gritting their teeth'! It is easy to make such unintentional statements. Many in the TV industry find it hard to believe that forecasters do not have a script or autocue, but the fact is we don't; I suppose our charts are our prompts. It can lead to spoonerisms, such as 'drain and rizzle', 'frog and fost' or 'fist and mog', but thankfully I have not yet done the same with 'mist patches'. I also avoid tongue twisters such as 'short sharp showers to the south of Sheffield'.

Many incidents could only have happened in Yorkshire. I remember once telling a farmer it was going to rain that coming night. When he rang up the next morning I asked, 'Did you have any rain in the night?' Back came the reply, 'Nay lad I don't get up in t' middle of t' night to see if it's raining!' Another favourite memory is of the farmer who phoned me and exclaimed: 'It wor so windy last night that it blew the gate away and left just the paint.'

Then there was the gentleman who rang for a barometer reading and I innocently enquired, 'Do you want it in millibars or inches?' The response was distinctly abrupt: 'I want it in Pudsey young man!' We are often asked for readings in order that barometers can be set, and I have been known to suggest with tongue in cheek that they stick the instrument in a bucket of water so that it should then point to 'Wet'.

I once had a phone call from a man in Filey complaining that his line must be crossed with ours. Often, just as he was going out to work, some bloke kept ringing up and asking if the coast was clear. He was sick of telling him he had the wrong number – and every time it happened his wife's face turned pink!

Most touching was the lady who wrote to say she was very hard of hearing and so didn't try and listen to what I had to say. Instead she just to looked to see if I was smiling, in which case she knew the weather would be fine.

Andrew Pearson

It's the beginning of the last day of
September at Sibsey, north of Boston,
and the rising sun highlights the mist
that has formed overnight. Sibsey
Trader Windmill is fully working and
still stone-grinds flour to this day.

THE CALENDAR YEAR

The photographs on the following pages have all been submitted by viewers of *Calendar*. It therefore seemed appropriate that they should be arranged in calendar order, beginning not in January but in April. They thus form a pictorial journey through the seasons from the onset of what admittedly is often a cold and wet spring, taking in summer and the glories of autumn, and ending with the striking contrasts that winter can bring in its wake. It may come as a surprise that February has produced by far the greatest number of photos in this selection – and August the least!

Although concentrating primarily on the weather and its many moods, these images also capture the amazing variety of the area served by Yorkshire Television. They provide a snapshot to dip into and enjoy at all times of the year!

APRIL

John Morley

The water-cycle in action!

John remarks: 'My wife and I had been walking near Bakewell in good weather conditions, but abandoned the full walk when the heavens opened. When we saw this scene we thought the moor was on fire but then we realised the smoke was in fact steam.'

This is known as 'steam fog' caused by the warm sunshine evaporating the moisture on the moor. The air up to a few feet above the ground is saturated and cannot hold any more water vapour (which is invisible), the excess moisture condenses into water droplets and looks like 'steam'. This will soon evaporate once more only to condense again into cloud droplets at a higher altitude and eventually produce more showers which will soak the ground and the warm sun will come out and … I think you get the idea!

Bob Carter

I remember passing a remark on *Calendar* how difficult it was to capture wind in a still photo. Subsequently I received this image showing perfectly a good westerly force 6 to 7 on the Humber. I hope the bridge windows are closed!

Ken Jacobs

This is the familiar power-station generated cumulus or 'fumulus' over Drax Power Station. Also of interest in this scene taken near Winteringham are the wisps of thin stratus or possibly particulate pollution clouds that have begun to form into undulating waves as the sun warms up the atmosphere on this chilly April morning.

Bob Carter
Lightning over the Lincolnshire Wolds, looking south-west from the Humber estuary.

Jeff Briggs
I'm often asked how the moon and sun can be visible in the sky at the same time. The simple answer is that, apart from the sun, the moon is the brightest object in the sky (although it simply reflects the sun's light). Consequently twice a month around the 'half moon' phases, the moon will be quite visible in the daytime blue sky. In Jeff's photo, taken in Bradford, the moon is waning (becoming smaller or more 'crescent' in its phase). Over the next few days it will seem closer to the sun in the sky making it more difficult to see due to the proximity of the sun's glare. The cirrus cloud will be more transient and it's life cycle will be much more fleeting and more difficult to predict.

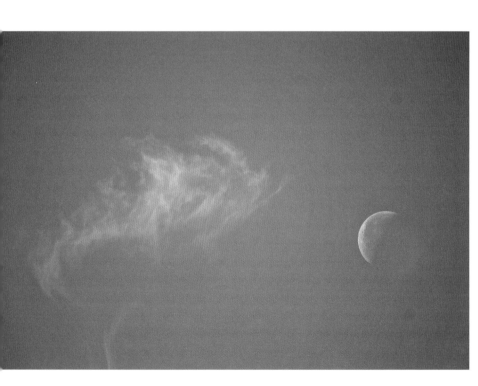

Jeff Briggs

Black snow! Jeff pointed his camera up to the sky during a snowstorm over Bradford (Good thinking Jeff, I wouldn't have even thought of doing that!) Look what happened – the snow turned black! The camera's auto exposure is compensating for the bright sky thus rendering the snow darker.

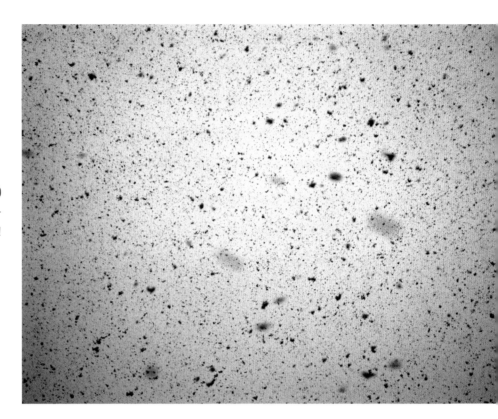

Thelma Burrus

It's tempting to say Thelma has caught the whole rainbow here at Beeford, but a whole rainbow describes a whole circle! It's possible to see this when using a hosepipe on a sunny day, or occasionally from a plane in flight. Maybe there are two pots of gold though!

Philip Moon

Cumulus over the Cow and Calf Rocks, Ilkley. The 'Cow', once claimed to be the largest detached block of stone in England, is traditionally linked with the giant Rombald. It is claimed that he slipped when taking a colossal stride from Almscliffe on the opposite side of the valley, leaving a depression at the foot of the 'Cow' resembling an enormous human foot. The cumulus cloud formations mirror other undulations in the gritstone rocks. In fact if you screw your eyes up, hold the picture at arm's length and cock your head to one side, that cloud above the 'cow' could be Mickey Mouse? No? OK, maybe not, moving on …

Ken Jacobs

This scene at Winteringham is like an approaching Armageddon. A bubbling, boiling, torrid cauldron of cloud that is sure to produce heavy downpours and possibly thunder. 'Bring the washing in Mavis it's going to chuck it down…'

Mick Wilson
A thoroughly wet day at Pontefract races.
Number thirteen there is rather frisky; the jockey
is having to 'rain' him in! I should think the going
was 'heavy' like the rain!

MAY

Thomas Cavell

Sunset over Thorpe Marsh power station at Barnby Dunn near Doncaster. The setting sun is illuminating the underside of the alto-cumulus which in turn is reflecting in the River Dun Navigation, not to be confused with the River Don, which runs nearby. In volcano terms Thorpe Marsh is extinct. Those cooling towers haven't issued forth clouds since it closed in 1994.

Collette Mellor

These chaps on Filey beach are oystercatchers, catching not oysters but the first rays of sunshine on this warm May morning. Many are standing on one leg. I wonder why birds do that? In fact oystercatchers are not known to eat oysters, tending to favour mussels supplemented with crustaceans, worms and insects.

Steve Cook
Late May Bank Holiday Monday 2008 was a sunny but very windy day. Gale force north-easterly winds blew down trees inland and at Cleethorpes piled up the sand against the sea wall. I'm willing to bet it was blown onto the promenade, across the road and into the town as well.

Peter Scott
'Ne'er cast a clout 'til may be out.' The hawthorn blossom is common in the spring, and this is a fine example at – er – Thorne in South Yorkshire. The name 'haw' derives from 'hage', the Old English for 'hedge', and many miles of hedges were planted in the English countryside during the enclosure period of the late eighteenth and early nineteenth centuries. A 'clout' is an item of clothing and one shouldn't even think of divesting oneself of a clout until the hawthorn, or may, is firmly out!

Harold Turner
This is a lazy, hazy late spring day near Beverley. The rape is certainly striking; a lovely sight for some but a sight for sore eyes if one is a hay-fever sufferer like me! The black seeds from the rape are crushed and can be used for animal feed, vegetable oil for cooking or for biodiesel fuel. Achoo! Bless you.

Gary Richardson

This is another shot I received after my request for 'wind' photos. These guys are fair motoring. Indeed, a windsurfer holds the world speed record for any wind-powered sailing craft. At the time of writing it is 90.9 km/h (56.5 mph) over a 500 metre course.

JUNE

Paul Thompson

The devastating floods of 2007 are well documented. The focus is often on South Yorkshire and Hull, but many other places were badly hit, including here in Louth, where the River Lud burst its banks.

Julian Rowe

This scene in Church Street at Darton near Barnsley captures dramatically the force of floodwater. This water is clearly running at a swift pace; flowing water is a force to be reckoned with and can easily sweep a person off their feet with possible tragic consequences.

Wendy Jones

This doesn't bode well for a nice day. Mist and fog has formed in the Calder valley overnight under largely clear skies, but an approaching warm front has increased high altostratus cloud enough to blot out the sun and so frustrate the mechanism for burning off the fog. All that will shift it now is a breeze in order to mix the saturated air with drier air from above. It'll probably be raining soon as well. So typical of June 2007!

Brian McCarthy

Poppies always add a splash of colour to an often otherwise verdant scene, as here at Thimbleby, near Horncastle. Brian said: 'I got well nettled mantling through the roadside verge to get this shot as I was wearing shorts.' I think it was well worth it Brian to capture the essence of rural Lincolnshire in such a dramatic light (but then again, I didn't get stung!).

Dom Taylor

Dom was taking pictures of a cricket match at Sewerby and was tapped on the back by a man who said to him, 'Maybe you should turn round and take a picture of Bridlington's first tornado!' It's unlikely to be Brid's first tornado, and it's unlikely to be its last, but well done Dom for capturing this funnel cloud which doesn't appear (at this stage anyway) to be doing any damage.

Dean Hayton

Dean is in the sunshine above the fret here, so he'll be nice and warm. But one thing is for sure – it'll be cold in the fret, or sea mist down on the beach at Ravenscar.

Bernard Branker

Sea fret, an east coast name for sea fog and here seen near Scarborough, can change a day at the seaside dramatically. Fret is a threat(!) usually between April and September. It forms when relatively warm and humid air passes over the notoriously cold North Sea. Water vapour (which is invisible) in the lowest layers of air condenses into water droplets (which are visible) and forms sea fog. As the on-shore sea breeze develops during the day, the fog or fret is brought ashore and the effect can be dramatic; Stripped to the waist and sweating one minute, fleece and jeans and shivering the next!

Steve Heritage

Is it a seahorse or is it a dragon appearing over Old Snydale, near Pontefract? That depends on your point of view (or your state of mind) but the *International Cloud Atlas* would quite correctly call it Cirrus Uncinus. Me? I think it's a seahorse. (Or is it a dragon?)

Ian Buley

This remarkable photo of a roll cloud was taken by Ian from the offshore support vessel *Putford Worker* on June 25, 2007 whilst at the Pickerill Gas Field thirty miles or so east of the Humber estuary. This was at the same time heavy rain was causing terrible flooding over many parts of Northern and Eastern England. So it would seem the weather was turbulent out at sea too.

JULY

Tom Rowley
Scarborough is noted for its spectacular sunrises of course, but Tom has also managed to capture a phenomenon known as a 'Sun Pillar'. This is a column of light beaming directly upwards from the setting or rising sun and caused by the sun's rays glinting off millions of ice crystals in high cirrus clouds. There is also a contrail and some alto-cumulus thrown in here just for good measure.

Joy Clayton
Flooding is deadly serious and during the summer of 2007 brought misery to many in our part of the world, but I remember Joy's photo taken in the Dearne valley raising a much needed smile at the time.

Robin Jackson

If we have sunny periods by day, do we have moony periods by night? The time exposure required to take this shot has allowed the clouds to move slightly giving a spooky feel to things over Braithwell, near Maltby, in South Yorkshire.

Brian McCarthy
It's alright; this is just a mini flood at Tealby!

Paul Haxby

Here is one of Paul's images taken from a para-motor. There is so much of interest in this shot, it's difficult to know where to start. It was taken over Goole looking east along the River Ouse towards Yokefleet and Blacktoft. The River Trent converges from the right to form the Humber. Just discernable in the distance is the Humber Bridge with Holderness and the North Sea beyond.

Matthew Porter
This looks like some kind of divine message from the gods. In reality it is precipitation (rain or hail) falling from a cumulo-nimbus cloud being illuminated by Scarborough's setting sun.

Eddie Whitehead
It's not often one can say there has been a hurricane over Scarborough! (in fact, to be technically correct, there can never be a meteorological hurricane over Scarborough). English Heritage was holding a Wartime Weekend spectacular event at Scarborough Castle and the Spitfire and Hurricane from the Battle of Britain Memorial flight gave a fly past.

Barry Smith
The classic dark sky of the cumulo-nimbus provides a contrast to the rainbow just offshore at Skegness. If you look carefully there is a secondary rainbow – something that obviously hasn't escaped Fido's notice.

Paul Haxby

Paul is a keen para-motor pilot and has sent me some wonderful pictures, full of meteorological interest. This is Barry Cheese, his fellow pilot (or judging by the skull and crossbones, should that be pirate?). Clearly seen are the tops of a layer of stratus cloud, through which are protruding the chimney and cooling towers of Drax power station. Condensed water vapour in the form of cloud droplets is issuing from the cooling towers – the very same stuff that is in the layer of cloud.

Kate Turner

A twister is visible behind the gate guard at Adastral Hall, RAF Cranwell, near Sleaford, on 19 July 2007. This was only one of a number of funnel clouds and tornados reported on this day.

Jane Sykes

Jane captured this tornado whilst leaving Flamingoland in North Yorkshire. Maybe she had been riding on the 'Twister' or the 'Corkscrew' perhaps?

AUGUST

Scott Sawyer

The contorted nature of the lightning spark – seen here over Lincoln – is always fascinating to study, something our ancestors, prior to the discovery of photography, would not have been able to enjoy. It is after all a fleeting phenomenon lasting only a fraction of a second, a rather dramatic fraction of a second it has to be said! The spark has to be imagined in three dimensions, not two, so that what appears to be loops are in fact the spark taking a route away from or towards the observer.

Sandy Brand'

God must be a Yorkshireman. Why else would there be a solar eclipse on Yorkshire Day? Although to be fair, the eclipse of August 1, 2008 was also visible from Lincolnshire, Nottinghamshire and Derbyshire. Oh and the rest of the UK and much of Europe. In fact the eclipse was total over parts of Arctic Canada, Greenland and northern Russia.

I was grateful to receive many pictures of the eclipse and this page shows a series of three taken over Pontefract. The pictures clearly show the moon passing between us and the sun. Someone once asked me if a solar eclipse was 'when the sun passed between the moon and the earth' Goodness me – if that ever happens we are all in big trouble!

Sandy used special filters to obtain these shots and I know I keep saying this, but I'm going to say it again. Don't EVER look directly at the sun, especially through a telescope or binoculars. You will be blinded – it's as simple as that.

The next partial solar eclipse visible over Yorkshire will occur on January 4, 2011, but there is only one type of solar eclipse really worth seeing and that is a 'total' one where the moon completely covers the sun's disc. The next total solar eclipse visible in Britain will not be until September 23, 2090, when there will be totality in south-west England. The next total solar eclipse in Yorkshire? October 7, 2135 – make a date in your diary!

Brian Holt

Brian captured this image of the precipitation process at work whilst sailing to Grimsby. You need to imagine this cumulo-nimbus cloud as a boiling, bubbling cauldron of air, water vapour, liquid water (rain) and ice (hail stones), the end result of which, in this case, is a soaking for Skegness. I wouldn't be surprised if there was a flash and a rumble in Skegness as well.

SEPTEMBER

Brian McCarthy

The farmer has been working hard, the harvest is in and the straw has been rolled into large bails at South Elkington, near Louth. Prior to 1992 stubble was often burned and was considered to damage hedgerows and trees and disturb or kill wildlife. The resultant smoke was sometimes a hazard to road traffic. The small cumulus and strato-cumulus clouds flitting across the sky gives us the familiar 'sunny intervals'.

Ian Patrick

It's been a chilly night with little or no wind and fog has formed over Bellwater Drain in the damp Fenland. Ian took this from Bellwater Junction Signal Box. What a charming place to work with a view like that; plenty of wildlife I would think, the call of curlew and lapwing, disturbed only by an occasional train to (or from) Skegness.

Matthew Williams
Matthew had to hang around a while to obtain this shot! As another day 'slides' to a close, the setting sun casts a rosy glow over Dalby Forest, North Yorkshire.

Bob Carter
Good weather for ducks! This intriguing shot was taken in the Queen's Gardens, Hull. Bob made his own rainbow, as anyone can, by having the sun at his back and letting the sun's rays play on the water spray (the finer the spray, or the smaller the water droplets, the more spectacular the rainbow). The duck gets a soaking, but does she mind? Not a bit of it! Water off a duck's back in fact.

Brian McCarthy

It's late September, the nights are drawing in and the gulls head home at dusk after a heavy day following the plough on the Lincolnshire Wolds. There is something I really like about this shot but I can't quite put my finger on it. Maybe it's the warm pastel colours, the soft sky promising a nice day to follow, or just the thought of going home to roost like the gulls?

Paul Haxby

UFO clouds! This is altocumulus cloud over Doncaster, but it is a very beautiful species of that genre known as 'lenticularis'. These are almond lens-shaped clouds, with a smooth layered form. The sometimes flying-saucer-like appearance of lenticularis undoubtedly accounts for several fake UFO reports. They develop downstream of mountain ranges, in this case the Pennines, in the smooth but undulating airflow (rather like downstream of a large boulder in a fast flowing stream). Even though the airflow through them can be fast, the cloud forms on the upstream side and dissipates on the downstream side thus appearing stationary in the sky. With me so far? Doesn't matter if you're not, just enjoy them for their delicate beauty. Glider pilots seek out this type of cloud as it affords them free lift.

David Townsend

The Trent Aegir is a tidal bore and is seen here at West Stockwith. September sees high spring tides (yes even in the autumn – honest) and as the incoming tide is funnelled up the ever-narrowing River Trent, a tidal wave develops. A similar one forms on the River Severn. The kayakers seem to enjoy it and of added interest here is the mist rising into the cold air from the relatively warm waters.

OCTOBER

Wendy Jones

It's an early morning in mid-October and Wendy has risen with the lark to take this photo of mist in the Luddenden valley. The lengthening nights and clear skies combined with light winds result in the temperature dropping sharply over the grassy slopes. This cold air, being denser, then sinks into the valley bottom, just as water would, and the water vapour in the air condenses into fog to form the 'Luddenden Valley Reservoir'.

Sandro Folegnani

There are numerous ways mist is formed and this is one of them. The waters of the River Don are relatively warm in October but the temperature of the air has dropped overnight and consequently the relative humidity has risen so that water vapour rising off the river condenses in the still air into mist – it's just like running a hot bath!

Jeff Briggs

These are cirrus clouds over Bradford. They are composed of ice crystals at about twenty five thousand feet altitude, which are precipitating downwards in a haphazard way showing the turbulent nature of the atmosphere at that height. This cloud's Sunday name is: Cirrus Floccus Intortus. Oh and that's the 9:30 Heathrow to Glasgow Shuttle leaving its own long and thin cirrus cloud.

Lisa Higton

A 'Cirrus Smile' This is a halo above Hillsborough, Sheffield, formed when the sun shines through cirrostratus clouds that are composed of countless tiny ice crystals. Each ice crystal, if aligned correctly, will refract the white sunlight and split it into its constituent 'rainbow' colours .Cirrostratus is the first sign of an approaching warm front so is often a sign of rain.

Paul Haxby

Not quite force 0 as in the picture below, this is more like Beaufort Force 1. Barry and Paul are once again para-motoring in the skies between Selby and Goole. This is Drax power station generating not only electricity on this October morning but also its own clouds above the cooling towers. The clouds from the towers are composed of water droplets and are often referred to in meteorological circles as 'fumulus' clouds.

Glen Sanders

On the weather chart the UK is under an anticyclone so there is little or no wind – Beaufort Force 0. According to my *Ladybird Book of Weather*, Beaufort Force 0 is indicated by 'smoke rising vertically' and that is certainly what is happening from the smoke stack at Cottam power station on the River Trent.

Steve Parker
Autumn is pasting its golden tints on a damp Roundhay Park, Leeds. There's rain in the air and it seems a long time ago since grandma and grandad sat on that bench eating a cornet!

Daniel Dunn
These are 'Crepuscular Rays' shining through the trees in Calverley Woods. They are simply sunlight illuminating tiny dust particles in the atmosphere. In reality parallel, they appear to converge towards the sun rather like railway lines do as they disappear into the distance.

Jeff Briggs
Clouds from an Aire
Valley power station
offer some drama to the
early October sun rising
over a distant bank of
stratocumulus cloud.
This was taken from
Bradford looking over
Thornbury and Pudsey.

Chris Toyne
How spooky is this?
The early morning mists
are rising up the Lincoln
Edge from the Trent
plain creating this
theatrical and menacing
Shakespearean scene.

Bob Carter
I would have simply pointed my camera upwards to photograph this Ferris wheel at Hull Fair in all its illuminated glory. Bob Carter knew better than that. He captured the reflection in the puddle (which wouldn't have been there if the weather had been – er – fair!)

NOVEMBER

Christopher More

'Scarborough was buzzing with people enjoying the warm afternoon' says Chris. It's not often one can say that during November in Scarborough. What's more the calm anticyclonic conditions have produced a super display of altocumulus clouds highlighted by the setting sun and casting the Bathing Belle statue into a striking silhouette.

Bob Carter

The Deep and the River Hull Flood barrier have been photographed many times but Bob has captured well the atmosphere of this water-front area of Hull including the moon and the red and green navigation lights reflecting in the water.

Terry Askew
The breakers are coming in from the northeast at Filey Bay, but the wind is blowing from the southwest resulting in spray being blown off the tops of the waves. Also in this dramatic shot can be seen the salt spray lingering in the air above the water. This salt-laden air is corrosive but it also contains the microscopic salt particles that act as condensation nuclei essential for the formation of cloud droplets and, consequently, rain.

Kim Gay
It's dusk on a November evening and everyone is heading home along the busy M62 near Lofthouse, Wakefield.

Paul Goodyear

Those golden leaves on the ground at Temple Newsam bring out the youngster in me. Don't you just want to run through them and kick them in the air? No? – Well if you don't want to, then I will…

Paul Adlam
Paul says: 'Instead of taking a picture of the sky, which one would normally do, I decided to capture the beauty of the setting sun reflecting against the glass on the building in Wakefield where I work.' Some nice reflective lateral thinking there Paul. I like it.

DECEMBER

Andy Nolan

The lengthening nights and clear skies combined with light winds result in the temperature dropping sharply over the grassy slopes between Queensbury and Bradford. This cold air then sinks into the valley bottom and the water vapour in the air condenses into fog. On the higher moorland the air is drier and less cold so is relatively clear. It was still cold enough for a touch of frost though.

Dave Bland
Herd of sheep? Of course I've heard of sheep, everybody's heard of sheep. The morning mist is lifting at Burnsall in Wharfedale and the sheep are waiting for their morning feed from the farmer. Just downstream of course is 'Baaarden' Tower!

Terry Askew
It has been a long December night (there is just over a week to go until the shortest day) and the sun is creeping above the horizon on its short, low journey across the winter sky. Bands of cirrus cloud above the lake at Bolton-on-Dearne add some definition to the otherwise clear sky.

John Paul Williams

High pressure is centred over the Low Countries (!) so the winds are light and overnight fog and frost has formed (in weather forecasts it is so easy to spoonerise this to 'frog and fost'). There is no sight of blue sky, so this frog and fost seen from Otley Chevin won't be lifting anytime soon. In fact it may well linger all day.

Allan Turford

It's only two days until Christmas – and a cold front has passed through in the night making everything in Palterton damp. The winter sun has reached as high in the sky as it can at this time of year but at least the nights are drawing out!

Gordon Nowell
The old mountain ash has seen better days
but the low winter sun gives a dramatic
light to the fells of Upper Wharfedale.

JANUARY

Michael Whitley

This wintry scene was taken at Langtoft in the East Riding of Yorkshire less than a mile from the North Yorkshire boundary at Octon. I wonder if the local hostelry really was open for food. It would taste delicious and on a day like this one wouldn't want to leave!

Eric Knowles

This is Coal Aston, Derbyshire, and that's a jack-knifed lorry. Thankfully, no one appears to have been injured here. It could have been nasty.

Paul Haxby

Paul is taking another flight in his paramotor over the flooded countryside around Barnby Dun after the heavy January rains of 2008. The redundant Thorpe Marsh power station is dominant alongside the swollen River Don and the River Dun Navigation.

Yvonne Holloway

Air Traffic Control have been busy overnight; the sun is about to rise over Sheffield 12. At 25,000 feet altitude the sun has already risen illuminating the aircraft contrails, some of which are spreading out to form cirrus clouds. At that time of the morning many aircraft are arriving in northern Europe having travelled overnight from North America.

Paul Gray

There has been a lot of heavy rain in the upper reaches of Wharfedale, swelling the River Wharfe considerably and the flood water roars over the weir at Otley on its way to the Humber estuary and the North Sea. This is mesmerising to watch yet very loud.

Dave Butler

Rain stopped play! According to Dave the River Calder floodwaters of January 2008 were still rising when he took this photograph. The groundsman will have his work cut out when the flood recedes.

Brian McCarthy

South Kyme Tower. Most will have heard the fairytale of Rapunzel ('Rapunzel Rapunzel, let down your hair…'). Well is this where she was imprisoned by the wicked witch? You never know! This shot is made all the more atmospheric by the presence of the jackdaws – you can just hear them chattering away as they do. What's the difference between a crow and a jackdaw? Well, if you see one jackdaw, it'll be a crow and if you see a flock of crows they'll be jackdaws. This is because jackdaws are gregarious birds and crows are more solitary creatures.

FEBRUARY

Guy Hageman

There is a chill wind blowing along the Humber and the smoke issuing from South Ferriby Cement Works tells me it's a stiff nor'easter! There was ice on the roads and Guy had just passed a car that had gone off the road so he stopped to check all was OK. Thankfully, all was well and just before he left he grabbed this striking photograph.

June Buckley

June says: 'I opened the curtains this morning to see a lovely double-heart shape in the frost at the top of our drive. I had heard my husband outside so automatically assumed he had had a romantic moment. When I enthused my delight at this gesture and asked how he had done it, my comment was met with a very puzzled look and he said he had no idea what I was talking about. He had surprised me a few days earlier with a bouquet of flowers for Valentine's Day - this being only the second one I had received in our forty-four years of marriage. As I am past the age of secret admirers I am now wondering who (or what) had done this most perfect shape. Could it simply be that someone has reversed into our drive leaving this secret message which has left me pondering?!'

Bob Woolley

The late afternoon sun is beginning to set casting a pink glow on Bolton Castle. Wonderful pile though it is, it must cost a fortune to heat (nice and cool though in the summer!). Notice the moss and lichen on the foreground rocks. Lichen, I'm told, only grows in an unpolluted atmosphere. Up here that's not hard to imagine.

Kevin O'Grady

Ewes near Rylstone in Upper Wharfedale! This is the time of year when a woolly jumper is essential. Sheep always look grubby against the sheer white of freshly fallen snow (especially if they've been tupped as some of these have!) and judging by that sky, there is more snow on the way too.

Richard Haxby

This surreal image shows an approaching snow shower on the North York Moors, and a heavy one at that. This is reminiscent of the classic photographs showing approaching dust storms in the desert, but something quite different is going on here. The air is blowing in from the Arctic and vigorous cumulo-nimbus clouds are generating snow showers on a squall line. Unlike a summer 'CuNim', which contains hail and rain, these winter examples contain snow flakes and lots of them. When the up-draughts can no longer support the flakes, the cloud dumps its load as in the picture, approaching with the prevailing wind. The snowflakes reflect light efficiently resulting in the appearance of a white wall. One minute the air is clear with bright sunshine and the next visibility is reduced to a few metres in blizzard-like conditions (possibly with thunder and lightning) only to return to crystal clear conditions minutes later: a nightmare for drivers and hill walkers. Light aircraft pilots will avoid them like the plague.

Guy Hageman

It's been a cold night over North Lincolnshire with freezing fog evident. Water droplets can exist in liquid form well below zero celsius and will not necessarily freeze until they come into contact with a solid surface such as a tree, car, TV transmitter or aeroplane. They then freeze instantly into ice crystals and deposit what is known as 'rime', here covering the trees and hedgerows.

Val Bolton

Incey Wincey didn't use string to make her web in Val's garden at Ossett. She used the finest silkiest gossamer (the spider, not Val!) as usual but on this particular night it became covered in rime. It is not until this happens that the number of spiders' webs become evident. In other words, they are always there but we don't always notice them.

Tony Fickes

Dave Bland

Graham Winter

On 19 and 20 February 2008, trees in many parts of the region were covered in rime. The views on the opposite page were taken above Wilsden (top) and on the Guiseley to Menston road, and this page shows the scene at Knaresborough. Rime forms when super-cooled water droplets of fog come into contact with a solid object whose temperature is below freezing. So what normally happens is the fog disappears from the air and the sun comes out creating these wonderful scenes. This is often confused with hoar frost, which is composed of ice crystals that form on clear still nights either as frozen dew or deposited directly from the water vapour in the atmosphere (in other words without involving fog). Still, whatever the cause, it looks nice doesn't it?

D. Robinson
Taken by Year 3 children from Lady Lane Park School, Bingley, in the school grounds.

Tony Fickes
The same cold snap that produced those wonderful displays of rime also resulted in some impressive icicles at Goits Stock Waterfall, Harden, near Bingley. The cold air had its origins in the high Arctic and was brought to us via Scandinavia and eastern Europe. High pressure became established over the UK resulting in the cold air stagnating and producing freezing fog and a spell of sub-zero temperatures.

Gerald Illingworth
Ice on the Leeds & Liverpool Canal at Riddlesden has produced some impressive patterns and swirls which are plainly lost on the bemused ducks who seem more interested in a potential feed from Gerald. Note also how the small amount of warmth from the boat has prevented the water from freezing in its immediate vicinity.

John Earnshaw

It's almost 11am and it must still be sub-zero on the thermometer because the frost is still clinging to the long grass in front of St. Mary, Lead – a tiny fourteenth century chapel standing alone in the middle of a field a mile west of Saxton, near Tadcaster. Nearby is the site of the battle of Towton – 'the bloodiest ever fought on English soil' – which brought the Wars of the Roses to an end in 1461.

Jeff Briggs

A picture at Simon's Seat in Upper Wharfedale taken in similar conditions to the view opposite. All the mist and atmospheric pollutants such as dust, smoke, soot and grit are held under the temperature inversion above which it is as clear as a bell. Magical, just magical.

Michael Osborne

This wonderful display of nacreous cloud over Headingley was observed on 16 February 1996. Nacreous clouds are stratospheric clouds forming in the stratosphere at heights of around 50,000 to 80,000 feet where the sun still shines for a significant period after it has set at ground level. The stratosphere is very dry (less than one per cent humidity) and consequently these clouds are very rare indeed. There has not been another display as dramatic as this over England since. This display was visible from Edinburgh in the north to as far south as the Midlands. The observer at Leeds Weather Centre commented at the time that they were visible in the sky all day but looked like normal cirrus cloud until after the sun set and then they betrayed their identity in such an impressive way.

Wendy Jones

This image sums up February 2008 very well with high pressure on the weather chart equating to very quiet weather conditions resulting in mist and fog sitting in the valley bottom – and with an absence of wind that is where it is going to stay. Above the temperature inversion, which acts like a lid keeping the mist and fog suppressed, the air is relatively clear and it is in this clear air at Mixenden above the Calder valley where Wendy stood to take this atmospheric shot.

MARCH

Richard Herron

This Christmas scene at Cleethorpes has come almost exactly three months too late for most people. Snow is far from unusual at Easter but Easter 2008 was just about as early as it is possible to be. The last time Easter Sunday fell as early as March 23 was in 1913. Easter can occur earlier than March 23; the earliest Easter ever recorded was on March 22 in 1761 and 1818. The next time Easter occurs on March 23 will not be until 2160, and a March 22 Easter will not happen until 2285! By then we'll all be pushing up daisies!

Sheila Robinson

The Easter 2008 snow came as a surprise to many (except us weather forecasters of course!). During a motorbike rally near Leeds, Sheila's son and family woke up on Easter Sunday morning to the tent practically flat on top of them due to the weight of snow. Ah, the joys of camping!

Tony Fickes

There has been a sprinkling of snow on Whernside and the magnificently restored Ribblehead station on the Settle to Carlisle railway line looks splendid in the early spring sunshine. Whernside is the highest point in modern day Yorkshire and the boundary with Cumbria runs along the summit ridge. In British Railways days the stationmaster at Ribblehead used to send weather reports to the Met Office. There is certainly plenty of weather at Ribblehead!

John Earnshaw

'Richard Of York …' It is just about possible to pick out all the colours in this rainbow at Lofthousegate, although I've never really been able to distinguish between indigo and violet. I say 'John's rainbow' since each rainbow is produced with reference to a definite point (the position of the observer). As no one distribution can be the same for two separate locations it follows that two people cannot see the same rainbow. In fact it could be argued, each eye sees its own rainbow!

Andy Brook

Andy took this extraordinary photo of a robin in his garden at Wakefield on Easter Sunday 2008. The scene is more reminiscent of Christmas than Easter. Did you know that robins used to be called 'redbreasts' in the Middle Ages, then they became known as robin redbreasts and subsequently just robins?

Jim Sweeney

The mist has once again formed overnight under the clear Derbyshire skies around Ladybower and, as ever, the sun is up and is in the process of evaporating it back into invisible water vapour as another beautiful early spring day develops in this most attractive part of our region.

Thelma Burrus
Coastal erosion. A combination of a strong northeasterly wind and a high tide is taking its toll on the low cliffs at Barmston on the East Riding coast south of Bridlington. This coastline is one of the fastest eroding in the world. The angry seas and large waves are a force to be reckoned with and the soft boulder clay soil is no match for such power and strength.

Eddie Whitehead
Surf's up at Scarborough! The isobars on the weather chart at Easter 2008 could be traced all the way back to Spitzbergen inside the Arctic Circle so there was a good northerly fetch down the North Sea making for a good swell as well as unseasonably low temperatures and Easter snow.

Andrew Ramsay
It's those visibility-reducing snow showers again, seen near Harewood.

Graham Timms
Car-wash Scarborough style! This puts a new slant on the term 're-spray'. The Audi will soon be doused in corrosive salt water and paint chipping pebbles, not good for a metal car but it makes for a great photograph (unless of course it's your pride and joy).

Rachael Ince
Brrr. It's still sub-zero on this north-facing side of Rombalds Moor, Ilkley. White Wells Spa and Café normally stand out like a beacon on the moor, but not in the snow. Can you spot them?

Paul Haxby
This is another of Paul's pictures taken from his paramotor. I've included this because it shows how Drax power station is producing its own microclimate. The clouds being generated by the cooling towers are composed of water droplets as in a regular cumulus cloud, but conditions on this particular day are such that the cloud is deep enough to produce its own light rain or drizzle. Again, imagine how miffed you would feel sitting under that when all around you are enjoying a bright day with wall to wall sunshine.

Bob Carter
This looks like the kind of photograph
that might be used to illustrate 'pollution'
or 'global warming'. That may be so, but I
simply think Bob has captured a nice
sunset over Saltend.

WINTERS PAST

YTV viewers end this book by looking back over forty years to the days when deep snow was an annual event – sometimes for weeks on end.

THE photograph shows myself and my friends helping to push a car up Piccadilly in the centre of Bradford. I am sure the year was 1969, either January or February. It was about 8.50am and we were going into work at the Road Transport and General Insurance Co (later to become known as General Accident), which was based in lower Piccadilly. We were shorthand typists and worked in the typing pool. I was seventeen and I am the one in the foreground hanging on to my brolly and holding the driver's door, posing at the same time as pushing!
Ann Frearson (née Dennison)

WINTER weather can occur in summer! I was returning from shopping in Yeadon on 2 July 1968 when the storm happened. The sky turned black as midnight and I started running home with my toddler in her pushchair. As the huge hailstones started falling I raced into the garage with the pram. The noise was absolutely deafening. When we eventually got into the house the hailstones covered in soot had come down the chimney and were piled up over the hearth and carpet.

The picture was taken in Newlands Avenue, Yeadon, about eight hours after the storm. The council eventually came with lorries and a loading shovel to clear it all away.

Doreen Waite

MY colleague and I were on duty as vets on 18 March 1969. After evening surgery we returned to his house where my wife Elizabeth – who was pregnant – had joined his wife for chat and coffee. We had not been there long when Elizabeth indicated she wanted to return home. In the car she said that she thought her waters had broken.

During the night we decided it was time to go to hospital so we headed for Barnsley District General in about three centimetres of snow, which had fallen over about three hours. Because there had been no gritting the car was sliding all over the place but we got there. The snow continued and a freeze set in. Early the next afternoon my elder son was born and we later heard the news that cables had become heavy with frozen ice, had snapped and the Emley Moor transmission mast had fallen.

Freddie Marshall

IN December 1981 I had been in Spain and flew from Santiago de Compestela to Heathrow in heavy rain. Britain was immersed in cloud and only at about two hundred feet could we see that everything beneath us was covered in snow. We landed safely giving the pilot huge applause but stuck in the snow trying to reach the parking area. It was nearly an hour before our aircraft was dragged in. We were the last plane to land for several hours.

I reached King's Cross by underground to find the station in chaos. It was about 4.30pm on Sunday. Several trains from the Saturday had not arrived in London and many were cancelled. Eventually, some two to three hours late, a Newcastle and a Leeds train departed, both packed and with people standing in every coach. Our scheduled train to Bradford left one-and-a-half hours late at 7.30pm.

The rail journey took thirteen hours, with the last section from Wakefield to Leeds taking four hours! The steward had kept the buffet open to Wakefield, giving out many free teas and coffees until his stocks ran out. Outside was thick snow everywhere. As this was before the East Coast line was electrified, we were on a diesel HST.

Our train was terminated at Leeds. I caught a connecting local service to Shipley and walked home to Saltaire. I arrived home at 9.30am,

thirty minutes after I should have been at work and nineteen hours after leaving Spain! I took the day off to recover.

Next day I walked to work through the deep snow and it was four days before I dug out my car. I also had a big hole in my kitchen ceiling from water that had frozen in the bathroom's cold-water tank and then overflowed as soon as the temperature increased.

The photographs show deep snow in Saltaire and on the nearby Leeds & Liverpool Canal. Sadly, the Metro Waterbus service along the canal from Saltaire to Bingley no longer operates, although the signs are still in place.

Keith Preston

I MARRIED at St James the Great, Pudsey, on 18 April 1981, which was Easter Saturday. During the week prior to my wedding – and on my actual wedding day – the weather had been extremely warm and sunny. The following Monday my new husband and I flew from Leeds-Bradford airport to Majorca for our honeymoon. We were pig sick as the weather in Majorca was very cold and it rained heavily every day we were there. We did say at the time that we should have gone to Scarborough as the weather was beautiful when we left Leeds.

We flew home to Leeds-Bradford airport a week later. About thirty minutes prior to landing the pilot told us there was snow in Leeds and conditions were so bad that we were unable to land either there or in Manchester, as there was no way we could be transported over the Pennines back to Leeds. We could not believe it and finally landed at East Midlands airport. We did think at the time that the pilot was pulling our leg. When we arrived at our new home in Pudsey we had about two feet of snow up to the door and the guttering had fallen down.

We could not believe all this as the weather had been so hot prior to our departure.

Christine Ford

Jon Mitchell comments:
I can empathise with Christine completely because Easter 2007 was similar in many respects. On Maundy Thursday I presented a weather feature on Calendar that involved me dressed up as a 'split' personality. The left half of me was wearing a t-shirt, shorts (or more accurately 'short') and a flip – or was it a flop! On my right half I had a welly-boot, long trouser and a raincoat (or half of one anyway!). I was sitting on a deckchair thus attired, the idea of the story being 'Where would you rather be this Easter weekend? Bridlington or Benidorm?' The irony was that 'Brid' was forecast to be dry, sunny and warm, whereas Benidorm was expected to be wet and cloudy.

The forecast proved to be correct, but all the way through the presentation I wore a false smile because I was only too aware that as a family we had booked an Easter break in Majorca. It was frustrating sitting under grey and cloudy skies in the Med, whilst at home it was 'cracking the flags'! Ah well – Que sera, sera. Another glass of Sangria anybody?

Also by Great Northern Books

ESSENCE OF THE YORKSHIRE COAST

By Malcolm Barker

A beautifully illustrated book, featuring recently discovered archive photography.

This book goes behind the scenery to look in depth at life and work along the coast. It puts a new perspective on such subjects as fishing, smuggling, shipping and shipwrecks, and the proud story of lifeboats putting to sea in conditions of dire peril. It focuses on communities large and small, ranging from trawling out of Hull to the traditional fishing village of Staithes, and from Scarborough in its heyday to life at remote Spurn Point.
Fully illustrated. Hardback.

ESSENCE OF WHITBY

By Malcolm Barker

A superbly researched and beautifully illustrated book that looks in depth at the history of this popular seaside town. Glorious photographs enhance Malcolm Barker's illuminating, informative text.
Fully illustrated. Hardback.

MOUSEMAN

The Legacy of Robert Thompson of Kilburn

By Patricia Lennon and David Joy

This new book incorporates a history of Robert (Mousey) Thompson, a guide to some of his most famous pieces of furniture across the UK and information on how to identify and date Mouseman furniture.
A beautiful, hardback, large format, full colour book.

YORKSHIRE IN PARTICULAR

An Alternative A-Z

Edited by Michael Hickling

Foreword by Gervase Phinn

Asked to 'spell out' the essence of Yorkshire, journalists on the county's leading newspaper, The Yorkshire Post, have gathered together a diverse selection of people, places, products and peculiarities. The result is a book that will be treasured by all who have a special affection for this fascinating region.
Fully illustrated. Hardback.

A YEAR OF FAMILY RECIPES

by Lesley Wild

Customers at Bettys and Bettys Cookery School have been asking for a cookery book for years. A Year of Family Recipes is a personal collection of over 100 recipes by Lesley Wild from the Bettys family.
This 260 page hardbacked book covers everything from bread and jam making to suppers and salads; home baking and sophisticated entertaining.
Stunning photographs. Hardback.

Visit www.greatnorthernbooks.co.uk